ORFF ORCHESTRATIONS

GRADE 6

SPOTLIGHT on MUSIC™

SERIES AUTHORS

Judy Bond

René Boyer

Margaret Campbelle-Holman

Emily Crocker

Marilyn C. Davidson

Robert de Frece

Virginia Ebinger

Mary Goetze

Betsy M. Henderson

John Jacobson

Michael Jothen

Chris Judah-Lauder

Carol King

Vincent P. Lawrence

Ellen McCullough-Brabson

Janet McMillion

Nancy L.T. Miller

Ivy Rawlins

Susan Snyder

Gilberto D. Soto

Kodály Contributing Consultant
Sr. Lorna Zemke

Mc Graw Hill Macmillan McGraw-Hill

ACKNOWLEDGMENTS

Grateful acknowledgment is given to the following authors, composers, and publishers. Every effort has been made to trace the ownership of all copyrighted material and to secure the necessary permissions to reprint these selections. In the case of some selections for which acknowledgment is not given, extensive research has failed to locate the copyright holders.

Mayim, Mayim (Water, Water), Copyright E. Amiran, ACUM, Israel.
Arrangement copyright 1996 by earthsongs.

Macmillan/McGraw-Hill School Division
2 Penn Plaza
New York, New York 10121

Printed in the United States of America
ISBN: 0-02-295869-X
 3 4 5 6 7 8 9 045 06 05 04

Table of Contents

Introduction

The Orff approach to music education actively involves students in speech, movement, singing, instrument playing, and drama. Developed by the German composer Carl Orff (1895–1982), the approach is based on the instinctive learning behavior of children. Improvisation and movement permeate the learning process, and the use of specially designed Orff instruments enables children to create and perform ensemble music at every level.

The materials used include both folk and composed music, along with chants, rhymes, and poetry. As students experience this music, they develop a musical vocabulary and skills that may then be used to create original works.

Orff orchestrations have been created for selected songs in SPOTLIGHT ON MUSIC. Along with each orchestration are teaching suggestions. The teaching suggestions include:

Instrumentation—All parts except timpani are commonly written in the treble clef. Bass xylophone and bass metallophone sound an octave below the written pitch. Soprano xylophone, soprano metallophone, and alto glockenspiel sound an octave above the written pitch. The soprano glockenspiel sounds two octaves above the written pitch. The alto xylophone and alto metallophone sound at the written pitch.

Teaching the Orchestration—A suggested basic teaching sequence is given for each orchestration. In orchestrations, the bass part is usually the most important. Students must be secure with this part before other parts are added. Except for the bass pattern, most parts may be considered optional. The teacher may choose to use only some of the suggested orchestration depending on circumstances—such as ability of students, time available, or the accessibility of specific instruments. Many of the arrangements can be musically satisfying with only the bass part and one other part added for tone color and/or rhythmic interest.

Form—Suggestions for the final form may include introductions, interludes, codas, chants, and opportunities for improvisation.

Noteworthy—This is a list of important musical elements that can be reinforced with the orchestration.

The Orff approach can infuse music classes with a spirit of cooperation and joy, enabling students to develop concentration and perception skills, increased aesthetic awareness and physical coordination, and a high level of motivation.

General Suggestions

1. Teach one pattern at a time. Allow students to take their time in learning each part. They should feel comfortable with singing the song while playing a pattern before adding the next pattern.

2. Teach each pattern through movement, with the song. Have students:

   • Mirror you in doing each new rhythm pattern with body movement—preferably large locomotor movements (walking, jumping)—especially for parts that occur on the beat and/or the strong beat. Others can be done with body percussion patterns you create (clapping, patting and/or stamping) or mirroring you in doing the movements required to play the part on the instrument.

   • Sing the song, doing the pattern in movement.

   • Remove any unused bars on pitched instruments, to make understanding and playing the patterns easier.

   • Form groups of three or four students around any available instruments and take turns playing the pattern. (Later, the pattern can be assigned to the instrument indicated in the score. At this time, you only want to give all the students an opportunity to learn the pattern and to help others in their groups to learn it.)

3. After teaching the most basic part, add other parts one at a time. Have students:

   • Sing the song, watching and listening as you play each new pattern.

   • Form two groups and sing the pitches or say the rhythm of the pattern while doing the pattern in body percussion (or by mirroring you) as the other group sings the song and plays previously learned patterns. Switch roles for the groups and repeat. (Use speech patterns given, or create your own. Patterns occurring only on the beat and strong beat, or on a single note—such as at the ends of phrases—can usually be taught without spoken patterns.)

   • All together, sing the song while doing the pattern in body percussion (or mirroring you).

   Clarify pitches played, or learn about instrument technique as needed. Take turns playing the pattern while singing the song.

4. Relate the accompaniment to the lesson focus. Have students:

   • Recognize and describe ways that the accompaniment connects with and relates to the musical focus of the lesson. (It is important for students to realize what they are learning musically and how playing the accompaniments contributes to this.)

   • Review this connection each time you work on the orchestration.

5. Perform the accompaniment as indicated in the score, or as adapted by you and the students. Have students form groups at each instrument needed and take turns playing each part with the song.

Hullaballoo Balay

English Sea Chanty
Arranged by Brian Burnett

Hullaballoo Balay (page 2)

Hullaballoo Balay (page 3)

Yüe líang wan wan
(Cresent Moon)

Folk Song from China
Arranged by Marilyn Copeland Davidson

Yüe líang wan wan (page 2)

6

Tina Singu

Song from Lesotho
As Sung by Kathleen Hill

Tina Singu (page 2)

Part 1: wat-sha, Ti - na, Ti - na sing - u le-lu-vu-tae - o. Wat-sha, wat-sha,

Tina Singu (page 3)

O•3

Chiribim

Traditional Yiddish Song
Arranged by Judy Bond

1. Now when I tell you l' - cha do - di, you will all say Chi - ri - bi - ri - bim, And
2. when I tell you Lik - rat ka - la, you will all say Chi - ri - bi - ri - bom.

l' - cha___ do - di, Chi - ri - bi - ri - bim, Lik - rat___ ka - la, Chi - ri - bi - ri - bom.

O•4

Mi caballo blanco
(My White Horse)

Words and Music by Francisco Flores del Campo
English Words by Linda Worsley
Arranged by Brian Burnett

Mi caballo blanco (page 2)

14

Mi caballo blanco (page 3)

Mi caballo blanco (page 4)

Jikel' Emaweni
(Throw It in the Slope)

South African Folk Song - Xhosa
Arranged by Cheryl Lavender

Alternate pitched and unpitched percussion parts between A and B sections as you choose.

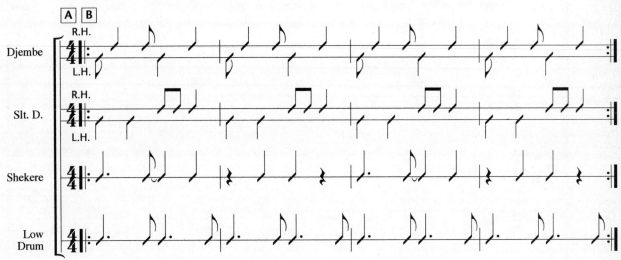

(Bass part may be divided between two players)

Mayim, Mayim

E. Amiran
Arranged by Nancy L.T. Miller

18

Mayim, Mayim (page 2)

Voice: Wa - ter, wa - ter, wa - ter, wa - ter, Hey! wa - ter, hap - pi - ness!

Voice: wa - ter, wa - ter, wa - ter, wa - ter, Hey! wa - ter, hap - pi - ness.

Mayim, Mayim (page 3)

Mayim, Mayim (page 4)

Mayim, Mayim (page 5)

22

Round and Round

Anonymous
Arranged by Judy Bond

Doney Gal

American Cowboy Song
Arranged by Virginia Nylander Ébinger

Voice: We're a-lone, Don-ey Gal, in the wind and hail. Got-ta drive those

GRADE 6

Doney Gal (page 2)

do - gies__ down the trail. We ride the range from

25

Doney Gal (page 3)

sun   to   sun,   for   a   cow - boy's_   work   is   nev - er

Doney Gal (page 4)

Doney Gal (page 5)

Doney Gal (page 6)

Doney Gal (page 7)

bound   to   go.   Yes,   rain   or   shine,   sleet   or

Doney Gal (page 8)

Red Iron Ore

Boat Song from the Great Lakes Region
Arranged by Brian Burnett

GRADE 6

Red Iron Ore (page 2)

The Lumber Camp Song

Canadian Folk Song
Arranged by Brian Burnett

1. Come all you jol - ly fel - lows and lis - ten to my song; It's
2. At four o' - clock each morn - ing the boss be - gins to shout: "Heave
3. At six o' - clock it's break - fast, and ev - 'ry man is out, For
4. And then comes up the log - ger, all at the break of day: "Load

all a - bout the shan - ty boys and how they get a - long. We're the
out, my jol - ly team - sters; it's time to start the route." The
ev - 'ry man who is not sick will sure be on the rout. There's
up my slide, five hun - dred feet; to the riv - er drive a - way." You can

The Lumber Camp Song (page 2)

River of My People

Words by Pete Seeger
Music based on Traditional Russian Folk Song
Arranged by Virginia Nylander Ebinger

1. There's a riv - er of my peo - ple And its flow is swift and
2. Man - y rocks and reefs and moun - tains, Seek to bar its storm - y
3. You will find me in the main - stream, Steer - ing sure - ly through the
4. For___ I have mapped this riv - er, And I know its liv - ing
5. O___ riv - er of my peo - ple, To - geth - er we must

GRADE 6

River of My People (page 2)

River of My People (page 3)

Voice

course	is deep and	long,	Flow - ing to	some might - y
broth -	ers in the	sea,	But re - lent -	less - ly this
see	our cer - tain	home.	Far be - yond	the rag - ing
hold	me to my	course.	And the cour -	age that this
broth -	ers wait be -	low.	Has - ten on -	ward to that

3 parts Opt.

SG

AG

SX

AX

BX

Timp.

River of My People (page 4)

The Ship in Distress

English Ballad
Arranged by Brian Burnett

1. You sail - ors bold who__ plough the o - cean See dan - ger lands - men__
2. For four - teen days, heart - sore and hun - gry, see-ing but wild wa - ter and__
3. A full - dressed ship like the sun a - glit - 'ring came bear - ing down__ to__

The Ship in Distress (page 2)

nev - er know.   It's   not for ho -   nor___ or pro - mo - tion; No
bit - ter sky,   Poor   fel - lows, they   stood___ in a tot - er, A -
their re - lief.   As   soon as this   glad___ news was shout - ed, It

The Ship in Distress (page 3)

The Ship in Distress (page 4)

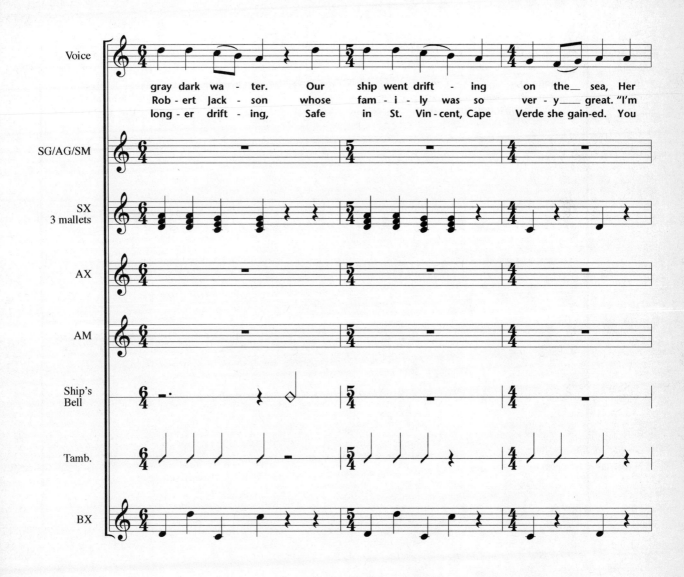

43

The Ship in Distress (page 5)

Yerakina

Greek Folk Song
Arranged by Virginia Nylander Ebinger

Yerakina (page 3)

Yerakina (page 4)

Yerakina (page 5)

49

El tambor
(The Drum)

Panamaniam Folk Song
Arranged by Doug Goodkin

El tam-bor, el tam-bor, el tam-bor de a - le - grí-a. Yo

* ○ = open, + = closed

El tambor (page 2)

quie-ro   que tú   me lle - ves   el tam - bor de   a - le - grí-a.

El tambor (page 3)

El tambor (page 4)

Voice/SX: - ta a - mi - ga mi - a. *Group* Yo quie-ro que tú me lle -

El tambor (page 5)

D.S. al Fine

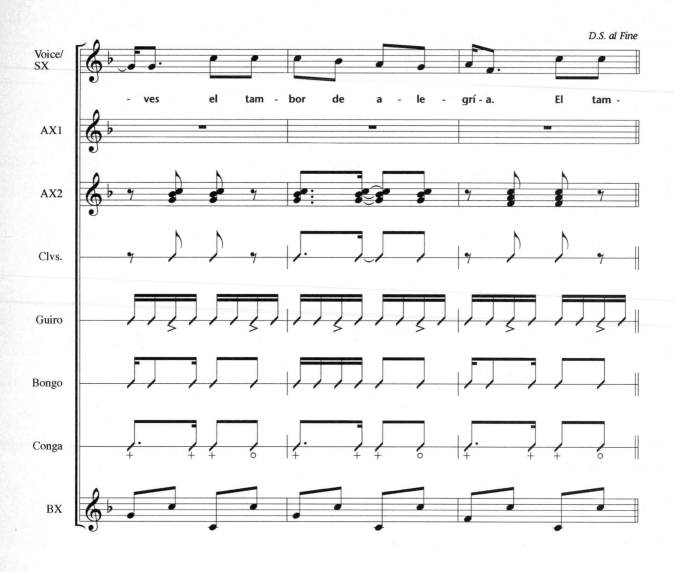

Voice/SX: — ves el tam - bor de a - le - grí - a. El tam -

GRADE 6

Jede, jede, poštovský panáček
(Riding, Riding, Is Mr. Postman)

Czech Folk Song
Arranged by Cyndee Giebler

Rid - ing, rid - ing, Post - man is rid - ing,

rid - ing, rid - ing is Mis - ter Post.

Jede, jede, poštovský panáček (page 2)

Blow - ing his horn, he calls, Bear - ing the trunk he hauls,

rid - ing, rid - ing is Mis - ter Post.

Troika

Words and Music by Dave and Jean Perry
Based on a Traditional Russian Folk Song
Arranged by Judy Bond

1. Through the night the wind is blow-ing, swirl-ing 'round the fall-en snow,
2. Swift-ly, now the sleigh is fly-ing; From the for-est to the town,
3. In the hall the peo-ple danc-ing; Sounds of laugh-ter ev-'ry-where.

Rid - ing high up - on the troi - ka, to the vil - lage we must go.
Can - dles burn with cheer - ful bril - liance; Voic - es ring in fes - tive sound.
Play the bal - a - lai - kas to the beat - ing rhy - thms in the air.

Troika (page 2)

Voice: Hur - ry, coach-man, with the troi - ka, hur - ry, hors - es, through the snow,

to the win - ter cel - le-bra - tion, to the vil - lage far be - low.

(labels:) Voice, SG/AG, TB, V. Slap, BX

Refrain

Add sleigh bells

GRADE 6

Dere Geliyor
(River Overflowing)

Arranged by Judy Bond

Cape Cod Chantey

New England Sea Chantey
Arranged by Nancy Miller

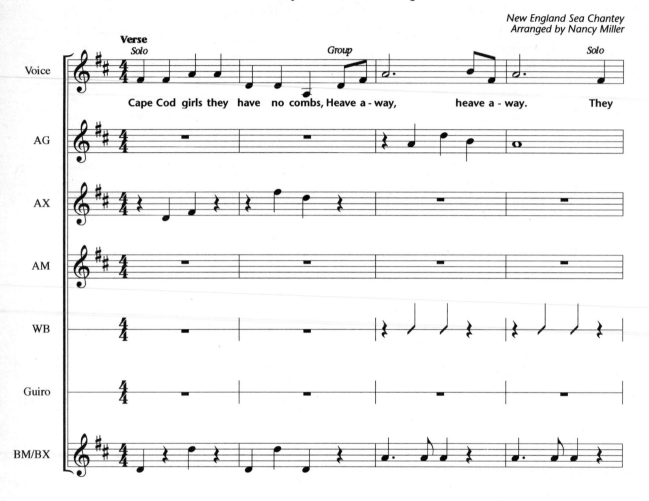

Cape Cod girls they have no combs, Heave a - way, heave a - way. They

Cape Cod Chantey (page 2)

comb their hair with cod-fish bones, We are bound for Aus-tra - lia!

Cape Cod Chantey (page 3)

Heave a-way my bul-ly, bul-ly boys, Heave a-way! Heave a-way!

Cape Cod Chantey (page 4)

Voice: Heave a-way and don't you make a noise, We are bound for Aus - tra - lia!

Do Lord

African American Spiritual
Arranged by Marilyn Copeland Davidson

Do Lord (page 2)

Do Lord (page 3)

do re-mem-ber me.   Way   be - yond__   the blue.

Player 2

Sometimes I Feel Like a Motherless Child

African American Spiritual
Arranged by Judy Bond

Sometimes I Feel Like a Motherless Child (page 2)

long   way___   from   home,_____   A   long   way___   from home.

Shady Grove

Southern Appalachian Folk Song
New and Additional Words and
Music by Jean Ritchie
Arranged by Margaret C. DuGard

Shady Grove (page 2)

Voice: Shad - y Grove, my lit - tle love, Bound for Shad - y Grove.

AG

AX

Cab.

TB

Guiro

BX/BM/Timp.

I'm Gonna Sit at the Welcome Table

African American Spiritual
Arranged by Robert de Frece

71

I'm Gonna Sit at the Welcome Table (page 2)

I'm gon-na sit at the wel-come ta - ble. I'm gon-na
I'm gon-na move those Jim Crow la - bels. I'm gon-na
I'm gon-na walk the streets of glor - ry. I'm gon-na
All God's__ chil-dren gonna sit to - geth - er. All God's__

sit at the wel - come ta - ble one of these days._____
move those Jim Crow la - bels one of these days._____
walk the streets of glo - ry one of these days._____
chil-dren gon-na sit to - geth - er one of these days._____

1., 2., 3.

GRADE 6

I'm Gonna Sit at the Welcome Table (page 3)

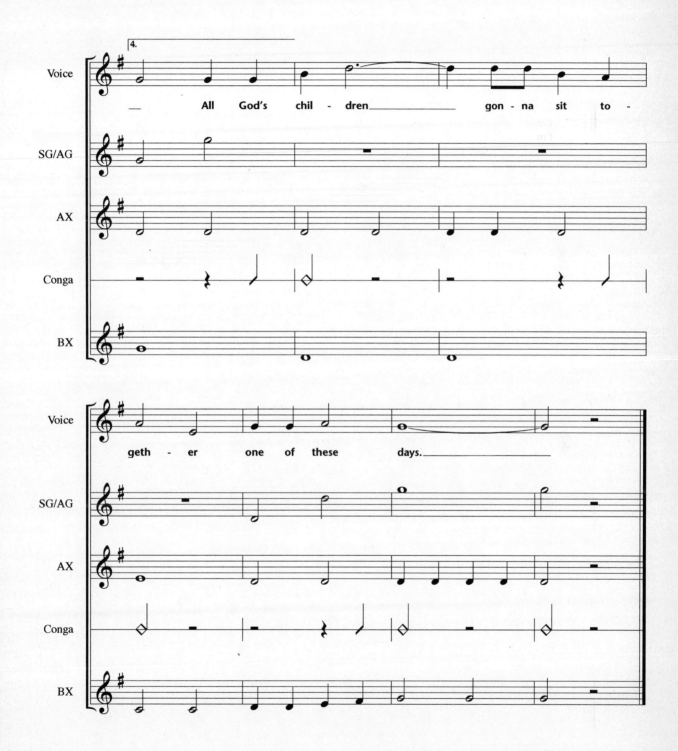

4.

Voice: All God's chil - dren_____ gon - na sit to -

geth - er one of these days._____